Trapped!

MALACHY DOYLE

Illustrated by Jane Cope

OXFORD
UNIVERSITY PRESS

OXFORD
UNIVERSITY PRESS

Great Clarendon Street, Oxford OX2 6DP

Oxford University Press is a department of the University of Oxford.
It furthers the University's objective of excellence in research, scholarship,
and education by publishing worldwide in

Oxford   New York

Auckland   Cape Town   Dar es Salaam   Hong Kong   Karachi
Kuala Lumpur   Madrid   Melbourne   Mexico City   Nairobi
New Delhi   Shanghai   Taipei   Toronto

With offices in

Argentina   Austria   Brazil   Chile   Czech Republic   France   Greece
Guatemala   Hungary   Italy   Japan   Poland   Portugal   Singapore
South Korea   Switzerland   Thailand   Turkey   Ukraine   Vietnam

Oxford is a registered trade mark of Oxford University Press
in the UK and in certain other countries

British Library Cataloguing in Publication Data
Data available

ISBN-13: 978-0-19-918417-0
ISBN-10: 0-19-918417-8

3 5 7 9 10 8 6 4 2

Available in packs
Stage 14 More Stories A Pack of 6:
ISBN-13: 978-0-19-918416-3; ISBN-10: 0-19-918416-X
Stage 14 More Stories A Class Pack:
ISBN-13: 978-0-19-918423-1; ISBN-10: 0-19-918423-2
Guided Reading Cards also available:
ISBN-13: 978-0-19-918425-5; ISBN-10: 0-19-918425-9

Cover artwork by Jane Cope
Photograph of Malachy Doyle by Peter G Dobson A.B.I.P.P

Printed in China by Imago

CHAPTER 1

Jacko

Jacko's mine. We were born on the same day, so that proves it. My dad says he's the best sheepdog the farm's ever had and that he belongs to him, but he doesn't. If Dad calls him from one side of the field and I call him from the other, you can bet who he runs to every time. Me!

He's a brave dog and he's a clever dog and I'll tell you why.

I love the farm but there's parts of it even I don't go on. That's because we live at the foot of a mountain and further up there used to be lead mines.

Over a hundred years ago there was a whole village up there. Three hundred people worked in those mines. Now there's nothing but a few piles of stones. Just quarry tips, broken down buildings and mine shafts.

They're really dangerous, those shafts. Never been covered over, see? If you didn't know where you were going, you could fall in. You wouldn't have a hope.

If the drop didn't kill you, you'd die of hunger. No one would find you because no one goes up there any more. Only Dad and Jacko and the sheep.

Dad knows the mountains better than anyone. He's lived on the farm all his life.

He's fenced off all the holes but he's always careful in case there's another one he doesn't know about, covered over by grass or loose boulders, or uncovered by a rock slide.

And Jacko, he's amazing. No chance of him falling down a mineshaft. Or so I thought.

CHAPTER 2

Jacko goes missing

One Friday evening, I'd just got in from school. I was warming myself by the fire, chatting to Mam after the long trudge up the lane from the bus. The sky was full of snow – the first that winter.

Dad drove into the yard on his quad bike. He'd just come down off the mountain, checking the sheep. I looked around, expecting to see my dog running behind as usual but there was no sign of him.

'Where's Jacko, Dad?' I called, hurrying outside.

'Isn't he here, son?'

Straight away I knew something was wrong. I shook my head.

'He was with me on top,' said Dad. 'I went to sort out a ewe tangled up in some wire. When I looked round he was gone. I called a few times but there was no sign. I thought he must be racing me down, like he does. It was nearly dark so I didn't want to hang about. Are you sure he's not here? Have you checked with your mam?'

I ran back inside.

'Mam, have you seen Jacko?'

'No, love. He's with your dad, isn't he?'

We searched the barns. All the while Dad was saying things like, 'Don't worry, Thomas, he'll turn up.' But I knew he was worried too. It wasn't like Jacko. He never went off by himself. And he always came to see me after school, first chance he got. If he wasn't out with Dad, he'd listen for the bus and come rushing down the lane to meet me.

'Something's happened,' I said. 'You'll have to go back up and look for him.'

But Dad said, 'Look, Thomas. I know you're upset but the light's nearly gone. No one goes up there in the dark, you know that. It's not safe.'

'What about Jacko?' I yelled at him. 'It's not safe for him either! We can't just leave him there.'

Dad sighed. 'Calm down, Tom. I'm sure he'll turn up. If he's not home by morning I'll go and look. All right?'

All evening I watched for Jacko.

I lay awake, waiting and worrying. It didn't bring him back.

CHAPTER 3

The search

I must have dropped off eventually, because it was the sound of Dad coming down off the mountain early the next morning that woke me.

I ran to the window, watching for Jacko, but he wasn't with him. I threw myself back down on the bed.

Jacko's more than a dog, see. A bit like a brother, really. The brother I never had.

Mam came up to my room. 'He couldn't find him, love.'

'I know.'

She held me close. 'He's a bright dog. I'm sure he'll find his way back.'

'Not if he's dead,' I said. 'Not if he's been hit by a lorry down on the road. Or if he was injured in a fight with a stray dog he found worrying the sheep.'

And then my real fear came out. 'Not if he's fallen down a mine shaft.'

'Oh Thomas, I'm sure it's nothing like that. He's probably just gone off to visit another farm or down to the town. Dogs often wander.'

'Not my Jacko. Jacko never does. Something's wrong, I know.'

Mam tried to calm me but I wouldn't have it.

I threw my clothes on and ran downstairs. Dad was still in the kitchen.

'We're going up again, Dad,' I said. 'I need to know.'

I gobbled my cornflakes while Dad finished his fry-up. I grabbed my wellies, my coat, binoculars and torch.

Dad looked a bit annoyed, having to go back a second time, but he didn't say anything.

We piled on the bike, Dad up front and me behind, and took off up the track. Sheep flocked towards us, thinking we'd brought them food, before turning away in disgust.

We drove round for hours, covering almost every inch of the farm. Anywhere the bike couldn't get to, we jumped off and searched on foot. We called, we whistled, I gazed into the distance with my binoculars, but there was no sign of him anywhere.

We were both getting cold. The snow hadn't started yet but there was a biting wind. Every time we got to one of the fenced-off mine workings, Dad went ahead of me and yelled for him. 'Jacko! Jaaackoooooo!' His name echoed down the hole and we'd listen for an answering bark. But it never came.

'We have to get back, Tom,' said Dad. I knew he was right. Cold and fed up, I climbed on behind him and we headed home.

I moped about the place all afternoon. Couldn't get stuck into anything. Tried reading but the book was boring. Who cares, I thought. Who cares what happens to these stupid people? I switched on the telly. Horse racing, some ancient film and an opera. Huh!

Three p.m. I flung my coat on, shouted, 'I'm off out!' to Mam, and stomped across the yard. I found myself walking up the track to the mountain.

I stomped on, furious with the world.
Kicking rocks, splashing in puddles,
getting as wet and mucky as possible.

I turned off the track towards the
main mine workings. I knew I wasn't
allowed there on my own.

I knew Dad would yell at me if he found out. But I couldn't be bothered about him. Couldn't be bothered about anything, except Jacko.

We'd been there already earlier, so it wasn't as though I was likely to find anything new. But something kept drawing me on. Despite the snow, falling gently. Despite the fading light. Despite the fact that I was already cold and wet from walking through all that mud and water. At least the wind had dropped, in the stillness that so often comes before snow.

Suddenly, way over to my left I heard it. A bark, his bark. Yes, there it was again. But a long way off, somewhere over on Will Evans' side.

'I'm coming, Jacko!' I ran to the fence, clambered over and raced full speed towards him. And then I fell.

CHAPTER 4

The fall

I landed on a pile of rocks at the bottom of a hole. I heard my arm crack and lumps of earth and small stones showered down on me.

It took me some time to get up. My right arm was killing. It was sticking out at a funny angle and when I tried to move it, the pain cut through me.

At least it was only a shallow hole, not a deep shaft, but it was still dark in there.

Looking up to the light above I worked out I must be three or four metres down. It was too far to climb with only one good arm. Freezing cold, with the night closing in.

Then I remembered Jacko. I called out his name and he barked, furiously. It sounded far away.

'Help!' I yelled a few times. But the only person who ever went up that way was old Will Evans. Fat chance of him taking a stroll around the mountain top in the dark.

Fat chance of Dad finding me either, even if he had realized I'd gone missing and was out looking. Only way he'd hear me was if he stood in the very spot I'd been where I'd heard Jacko, and the wind stayed down.

But even underground I could tell a storm was blowing up. I stopped yelling. It was just upsetting Jacko even more.

I knew I had to get out, quick, while I still had some hope of finding my way home. But what could I do?

Maybe if I piled up some rocks, and tried to climb up. It was the only way.

First I had a rummage round in my pockets. If my penknife was there, I could try cutting into the side, so there'd be something to hold on to. I found my torch instead, so I shone it round the bottom of the hole.

Rocks, rocks, and more rocks. I got to work, one-handed. My right arm was hurting like mad every time I moved. It took a long time, but I managed to edge the biggest rock over to the side.

Climbing up on it, I stretched as high as I could, but I was still a long way from the top.

Stepping back down, I set to moving the next biggest rock. Getting it over to the first one wasn't too bad but lifting it up was nearly impossible. After trying for ages I got it onto the first stone and thought I had it resting safely.

I climbed up, but it slipped off and I crashed back down, landing on my bad arm. I screamed.

Once the pain had calmed down,
I tried again and this time it worked.
Stretching on tip-toe, I could nearly reach
the top! I'd never get another rock up.

I had to go for it.

I shone the torch closely at the rock
face to try and find places I could put
my hands and feet. At full stretch I got
my good hand up onto a firmly fixed
stone and pulled with all my might.

Finding a hold for my right foot,
I swung my left round wildly. I felt a
higher stone to put it on and pressing
my body firmly into the rock face, slid
my hand upwards. I felt the snow on
top!

Moving my hand round carefully to
find a firm grip, I hauled myself
upwards. My right foot found the hold
it needed and I pushed down hard,
raising the other up to where my hand
had been. One final push and I was up.
I had to use both arms to scramble
forward, away from the edge, in case
I slipped back.

I yelled as the pain shot up through my arm. Jacko heard me and yelped.

'It's all right, boy ...' I started to say. Then I blacked out.

It was completely dark by the time I came round. I was freezing cold and if I didn't get home quickly I was in real trouble. There was no time to even think about Jacko.

I struggled to my feet and started to head for the farm. The snow was drifting so I kept sinking in, right up to my knees. My jeans were soaked through.

It was hard to work out exactly where I was, what with the dark and the snow. I was terrified it might have drifted so deep that it was covering the fence around a mine shaft and I'd fall straight in.

I trudged on for ages, getting colder and colder, until I could go no further. I stopped to rest in the shelter of a large rock and tried to calm myself down.

I thought I heard something and listened hard. Yes! It was the sound of an engine!

'Dad! Dad! Over here!' The lights of the quad cut through the snow but the engine drowned out my calls.

As I ran towards him he swerved to go round the rock.

'Stop, Dad! Stop!' I yelled at the top of my voice. The engine cut out.

'Thomas! Thomas! Is that you?'

I crashed forward into the snow, passing out for the second time.

CHAPTER 5

I know where he is

'Aaaahh!' The pain woke me.

Mam was by my side, in the back of the Landrover. 'It's all right, Tom.'

'My arm …'

'Yes, it's broken, love. We're taking you down to the hospital.'

'But Jacko? What about Jacko?'

'Try to stop worrying about Jacko, love. We've got to get you sorted out first.'

In the hospital, they put the arm in plaster and kept me in overnight. I didn't really care where I was. All I wanted to do was sleep. I came round at midday. Mam and Dad were there beside me.

'I'm glad it's your right arm anyway,' Mam said. 'You'll still be able to do your school work.' I groaned – I'm left handed.

It was only when she was helping me get dressed that I remembered.

'Jacko? Where's Jacko?'

Dad hesitated, like he didn't want to tell me. 'There's no sign of him, Tom.'

'But I know where he is!' I shouted. 'That's why I was on Will Evans' land, why I fell in. I heard him barking, I was trying to get to him! You've got to go and find him, you've got to go now!'

'All right, all right, Tom. Calm down. Let's get you home first,' Mam said.

The snowploughs had been out. Snow was piled up high all along the hedges and the fields were completely white.

Usually I loved the snow, but this time it made me angry, like it was part of the plan to take away my Jacko, the best friend I'd ever had.

But it was good to be home again. Mam made me up a bed on the big settee in the kitchen. I told Dad where I thought Jacko was and warned him to be careful, that Will Evans hadn't fenced in the holes on his side.

'I know, son,' he answered. 'I've been telling him for years.'

He didn't come back for the rest of the day. I could tell Mam was getting worried but she didn't say anything. The light was dropping before we heard the sound of the quad, cutting through the silence.

'Sorry I was so long,' Dad shouted through from the porch, stripping off his rain gear. 'The snow was too deep for the bike. I had to walk most of the way.'

'Where's Jacko?' I said impatiently, as soon as he stepped into the kitchen. 'Didn't you find him?'

'Oh, I found him all right.' His voice dropped, heavy. 'Bad news, I'm afraid, son. He's at the bottom of a shaft – a deep one.'

'Is he hurt?'

'I can't be sure but he doesn't sound too bad. A bit hoarse from barking so much.'

'How are we going to get him out?' I asked.

'That's the problem. He's a long way down and I don't think there's any other way in.'

'You'll have to climb in and get him,' I said.

My mother looked up in alarm. 'No!' she said to Dad. 'It's too dangerous!'

'But Mam,' I said desperately. 'What about Jacko?'

'Dog or no dog. Your lives are more important.'

'Give me a while to think about it,' said Dad, quickly. 'I'm sure we can do something. I'll go and have a word with Will Evans. Maybe he knows another way in.'

CHAPTER 6

No way out for Jacko

Later that evening, I woke up to hear Mam and Dad talking downstairs.

'No sign of Will up at the farm,' I heard Dad say. 'So I dropped into the White Lion, to see if he was there. Got talking to his mate, Hywel Davies. Hywel says there's no way we'll get Jacko out, said all the tunnels have caved in years ago.' His voice dropped and I strained to hear. 'He said the kindest thing to do is put poison down. Put Jacko out of his misery.'

'No!' I screamed. 'You can't! I won't let you!'

Mam rushed up. 'It's all right, Tom ...'

'He's my dog!' I yelled, loud enough for Dad to hear. 'If you kill him I'll never forgive you!'

I made them promise they'd do everything possible to get Jacko out. I told them to tell stupid ol' Will Evans and Hywel Davies that if they even thought of putting poison down we'd get the police on to them. I didn't trust them. Wouldn't put it past them to kill my Jacko just so there wasn't a big fuss about not fencing off the mine shafts.

The next day was Monday.

I was well enough to get up but they let me stay off school. Told me I wasn't even to go out of the house.

They said it was because I still needed to rest, but I knew the real reason was they thought the first chance I got I'd be up the mountain to check on Jacko. They were right too.

Dad was on the phone first thing.

The RSPCA said try the Police. The Police said try the Fire Brigade. The Fire Brigade said try the Mountain Rescue and the Mountain Rescue said they'd come!

Dad gave them all the details. They said they'd get everything together that night and drive down early the next morning.

I gave Dad a great big hug, I was so pleased.

Later I nagged Dad to bring me up on the quad to see Jacko, but he said with the snow so deep we'd have to walk a long way and I wasn't up to it.

'But you will let me go up with the Mountain Rescue?' I pleaded.

He knew there'd be no stopping me. 'All right, Thomas. Take it easy today and you can come with us tomorrow.'

He got another hug for that.

We were sitting round the kitchen table eating lunch when I suddenly thought.

'Dad, what about Jacko? He hasn't had any food since Friday. He'll be starving.'

'Oh, he'll be fine, Tom. Dogs can go much longer than that without food.'

I gave him one of my looks.

'All right, all right, son.' He sighed deeply. 'I'll take some up.'

'And a drink,' I said. 'Bring a bucket with you. You can fill it from a stream.'

Dad and Mam both raised their eyebrows.

'I'll be glad when that dog's back down in his kennel,' Dad muttered. 'I'm getting fed up with trudging up there in the snow.'

44

CHAPTER 7

The Mountain Rescue team

I was woken at seven thirty the next morning by the sound of a Landrover pulling into the yard. I ran to the window. It had Mountain Rescue in big letters on the side. Two women and a man climbed down and walked towards the farmhouse.

'You're bright and early,' I heard Dad say.

'Well, we always like to get started on a job at first light,' said Ali, the woman in charge. 'That way we get as long as possible to work on it.'

I threw on my dressing-gown and ran downstairs. We all had a cup of tea while Dad and I told them what had happened.

Jacko was barking frantically by the time we got there. He'd been doing it so much lately he'd almost lost his voice. It sounded sort of funny and sad at the same time.

'It's OK, Jacko,' I called. 'It's me, Tom. We've come to get you out.'

The rescuer, Dave, got ready to go down.

He put his gear on – helmet, boots, hooks, straps, the lot.

They drove a great big metal stake into the ground at the top and fixed the rope he was going to use on to that. Then off he went, abseiling down.

I called to Jacko, warning him. I hoped he wouldn't be too frightened seeing a strange man swinging towards him.

'Made it,' Dave soon radioed back up to Ali. 'But the dog keeps backing away. I think we might have trouble getting him in to the sling.'

'Did you offer him some food?'

'Yeah,' Dave replied. 'You'd think he'd be starving, but he won't come near it. We might need Helen down to give him a jab.'

'What's it like down there?'

'Seems to be a long passage leading off the main shaft,' Dave answered over the radio. 'Dog keeps heading down it.'

'I don't want him drugged unless they really have to,' Dad said. 'How about if I join them? I think he might come to me.'

'You ever done any abseiling?' Ali asked.

'Yeah, we did a bit in the army. I haven't got much of a head for heights but I'll give it a go.'

'Are you sure it's a good idea, love?'
Mam was looking worried.

'I'll be fine.'

Helen fixed Dad up with what he
needed. 'Just remember to swing well
out from the rock and you'll be OK.
Off you go.'

It took Dad about twice as long to get
to the bottom as it had Dave. I could
hear Jacko barking with joy at seeing
him again.

'Won't be long now,' Ali told us.

But she was wrong. Jacko still
wouldn't let them put him in the sling.

Dad spoke to Ali through the radio. 'I
think maybe we'll have to knock him
out after all. We can't do a thing with
him – keeps pulling away.'

'OK, Helen,' said Ali to the woman by
her side. 'Looks like you're going down.'

While Helen got ready, Ali explained
that she was a vet.

'Wait!' I said. 'Let me go too. Jacko's my dog. He'll come to me, I know he will.'

'Oh no you don't, Thomas Williams!' Mam grabbed me tight. 'No way are you going down that hole.'

'Please, Mam. I know what I'm doing. I abseiled on summer camp, remember?'

'Not with one arm, you didn't.'

'Look, Tom,' Helen broke in. 'You don't need to worry about the jab. It won't do Jacko any harm. It'll just knock him out for a few minutes so he doesn't struggle while we get him up.'

'But you don't understand,' I said. 'Jacko trusts me completely. He'd never hurt me, and he knows I'd never let anyone hurt him. If he's got to have an injection, at least let me be there with him. Mam, tell him. Mam?'

Mam looked worried again. She spoke to Dad over the radio.

'How safe would it be for Tom to go down?' she asked Ali and Helen.

'Oh, he'll be safe enough all right,'
said Helen. 'As long as he doesn't knock
his bad arm against the rock. Tell you
what, I'll go down with him and make
sure he's OK.'

'Is that all right, Mrs Williams?' Ali
asked. 'Helen's very good. Tom'll be in
safe hands.'

Mam nodded, but you could tell she
wasn't happy about it.

I punched the air with my good arm.
'Yeah!'

CHAPTER 8

A real star

After Ali helped me on with all the gear, I stepped back off the edge into the darkness. My mind returned to Saturday, falling, falling. I felt the panic rising but then I saw Helen, the ropes, and remembered where I was.

Jacko spotted me above him and started barking like mad.

'Shush, Jacko.'

Before I'd got myself free of the straps, he was jumping all over me, licking my face, my hands. And I was just as pleased to see him.

'Right, Jacko,' I explained calmly. 'We've got to get you out of here. We're going to put you in this sling and lift you up.' But he pulled away and ran off down the passage. Helen shone her torch after him. He was standing still, watching me.

'Come here, Jacko!' I said in my sternest voice. He crawled towards me.

'OK, everyone,' I told the others. 'Let's get him in.'

But quick as a flash he broke away once more, into the darkness.

I was just about to yell at him again when it clicked what was happening. He wanted me to follow him. Of course!

'What is it, Jacko? Is there something down there?'

I went after him. Somewhere behind
me I could hear the others. Dave was
telling Ali what was going on over the
radio.

In the torch light, with Dad beside
me, I followed Jacko along the passage.
It sloped steeply down. The air was
getting colder all the time.

Jacko disappeared through a narrow
hole in the rock. We waited for Dave to
go through first, just in case.

On the other side, we found ourselves in a great underground room, with a vast lake in the middle.

Jacko waited till everyone was through. Then he led us around the edge of the lake to a large rock and went behind it. We followed him and there, in a shaft of light from another hole high above, lay a man.

I pulled back, frightened, but Dad rushed over to him. 'It's Will Evans!' he gasped.

'Are you all right, Will?' There was no answer.

Helen reached him and knelt by the twisted body, feeling Will's pulse, checking for a heartbeat. Then she ripped off her coat and wrapped it around the old man.

'He's alive all right, but only just,' she said. 'Hypothermia by the look of it, never mind any injuries from the fall.'

Our eyes turned upwards to the daylight, way above us, at the top of the narrow shaft. 'We've got to get him out of here, quick.'

'What's hypothermia?' I asked Dad.

'It means his body's much too cold. They'll have to get him to hospital as soon as possible.'

Dave was already on the radio to Ali, asking her to call in the helicopter.

'Well I know who the real star of the show is,' said Ali, when all the excitement was over.

We were sitting round the table with steaming hot bowls of Mam's best stew in front of us.

'Who's that then?' Dad asked.

'Tom's dog,' she answered. 'If he hadn't heard poor old Will calling and gone to the rescue, that man'd be dead. No doubt about it.'

'So he's Tom's dog now, is he?' said Dad with a smile, ruffling my hair. And for the very first time I got the feeling that he really knew Jacko belonged to me.

And Jacko, curled up at my feet, snored contentedly.

About the author

I was out walking in the
hills, near where I live
in Wales, when an old
farmer stopped me.
'Watch out for the
mineshafts,' he said,
'they're not all
covered over.' He

told me he'd been on that same farm
all his life and that once, when he was
a boy, his dog had gone down one and
been trapped for two whole weeks. So
I went home and wrote this story.